For: Maisey

First published in 2016 by Rockpool Children's Books Ltd.

This edition published in 2016 by Rockpool Children's Books Ltd.
in association with Albury Books.
Albury Court, Albury, Thame
OX9 2LP, United Kingdom

Text and Illustrations copyright © Sam Walshaw 2016

For orders: Kuperard Publishers & Distributors

office@kuperard.co.uk | 020 8446 2440

Sam Walshaw has asserted the moral rights
to be identified as the author and illustrator of this
book. © Rockpool Children's Books Ltd. 2016

Printed and bound in Turkey

ISBN 978-1-906081-49-2 (Paperback)

rockpool
children's books

Albury Books

Sam Walshaw

Little Fairies

Buttercup's dancing shoes

It was breakfast time in the garden, and the fairies were enjoying their favourite breakfast of crumpets and fresh honey. Suddenly, a letter came through the letterbox.

Bluebell opened it.
"Oooh!" she exclaimed.
"We have all been invited
to a barbecue on the beach!"

"That sounds like fun!"
squealed Buttercup. "Let's go!"
The fairies got their things together
and set off. It was a long fly
to the beach...

...so they allowed plenty of time.

When they arrived, the sun was almost setting, and the fairies were ready for some delicious barbecue food.

They chatted with all their friends. There was music and dancing too, and the fairies were having a wonderful time.

Then Buttercup noticed
a little crab, sitting all alone.
He wasn't dancing or joining in.
He looked very sad indeed, so she
went over to see what
was wrong.

"Whatever's wrong, little crab?"
she asked gently.
"Why don't you come and dance
with all the other crabs?"

"I'm just so small,"
sobbed the little crab.
"I keep getting stood on,
and anyway I can't dance
like the other crabs."

"Oh dear,"
sympathised Buttercup.
"There must be something
I can do to help."

"No, I don't think you can help me,"
whimpered the little crab in a tiny voice.

Buttercup pondered a while,
and they sat together,
watching the moonlight
dancing on the water.

"See," said the little crab,
with a tear in his eye.
"Even the moonlight can dance!"

Suddenly Buttercup had a brilliant idea.
"Don't you worry, little crab!
I'm going to make you the best
and brightest dancer on the beach," she vowed.

"You'll see!"
The little crab
broke into a watery
smile. "Really?"
he quavered.

Buttercup flew over to Violet and Bluebell
to tell them all about the poor little crab.
"Oh no, how sad!" said the others.

"If you two will bring the little crab down to the
water's edge, I have a surprise for him,"
bustled Buttercup. "Okay, but what is it?"
asked Violet and Bluebell.
"Just wait and see!" she winked mysteriously.

Buttercup flew far out over the sea.
As the others watched, wondering
what she was doing,
Buttercup began to whisper
her magical spell.

"Twinkle twinkle, on the sea,
Make some dancing shoes for me.
Make them small and make them bright,
So tiny crab can dance all night!"

With a whoosh of her wand...

the tiny dancing
sparkles on the...

water began to rise!

They surrounded Buttercup like a whirlwind.
Then, as quick as a flash, they disappeared again!

"What happened?"
said the tiny crab, sadly.
"I don't think Buttercup's spell worked."
"Hmm, I don't know..."
admitted Violet, a little worried.

Just then Buttercup flew back to the
water's edge, where the little crab
was waiting.

And then they all saw that Buttercup
was clutching something. She held the tiniest,
brightest, most sparkly set of shoes
the little crab had ever seen.
"Go on, little crab," whispered Buttercup.
"Try them on, and see what happens!"

As the little crab slipped on
his glittering new shoes,
he started to dance! "Wow!"
he chuckled, with a big smile
on his face. "I can dance! I CAN!"

The tiny crab danced and danced all
night long, with all his little tiny feet,
and had an amazing time. Everyone danced,
ate and laughed together until sunrise.

In the morning, the fairies said goodbye
to all their friends. "Thank you, Buttercup,"
whispered the grateful little crab
in Buttercup's ear.

Then he handed each of the fairies
a beautiful seashell.
"If you put the shell up to your ear,
you can hear the sea," he smiled.
"When you hear it, you will always remember
how happy you made this tiny little crab!"

Contents

What is a butterfly?

A butterfly is a type of **insect**. Insects have three pairs of legs, making six legs altogether.

⇩The wings of a butterfly are covered in many tiny scales.

⇧The scales are usually patterned and coloured.

4

LifeCycles

Caterpillar to Butterfly

Camilla de la Bédoyère

QED Publishing

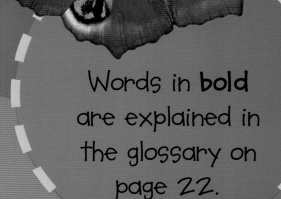

Words in **bold** are explained in the glossary on page 22.

A catalogue record for this book is available from the British Library.

ISBN 978 1 84835 923 9

Printed in China

Author Camilla de la Bédoyère
Editor Angela Royston
Designer and Picture Researcher Melissa Alaverdy

Picture credits
(t=top, b=bottom, l=left, r=right, c=centre, fc=front cover)

Corbis 17b Darrell Gulin, 19t Michael & Patricia Fogden, 20l Danny Lehman
Getty Images 4l Frans Lemmens, 5 Leroy Simon, 9b Kai Stiepel, 13b Kim Taylor & Jane Burton
NHPA/Photoshot 10l Kitchin & V Hurst, 10b Kitchin & V Hurst
Photolibrary Group 1b Wally Eberhart, 6b Earth Science Animals Animals, 7b Wally Eberhart, 8t Earth Science Animals, 8b Richard Day, 18–19 Don Johnston, 20–21 Radius Images
Science Photo Library 4r Pasieka, 22t Dr John Brackenbury, 23b Dr John Brackenbury
Shutterstock 1t SF photo, 2t Willem Dijkstra, 3t Markov, 6–7 Tina Rencelj, 6t SF photo, 7t Jacob Hamblin, 9t Tischenko Irina, 10t Kathy Keifer, 10c bhathaway, 11t Cathy Keifer, 11c Cathy Keifer, 11r Cathy Keifer, 11b Laurie Barr, 12–13 SF photo, 13t Jasenka Lukša, 14l Cathy Keifer, 14c Cathy Keifer, 14r, Cathy Keifer, 15t Jacob Hamblin, 15b Cathy Keifer, 16b Laurie Barr, 16l Laurie Barr, 16c Laurie Barr, 16r Laurie Barr, 17l Laurie Barr, 17r Jacob Hamblin, 22–23 Fizpok, 24t Jacob Hamblin

Insect bodies are divided into three parts.
The head is the front part, and has
the eyes and mouth.

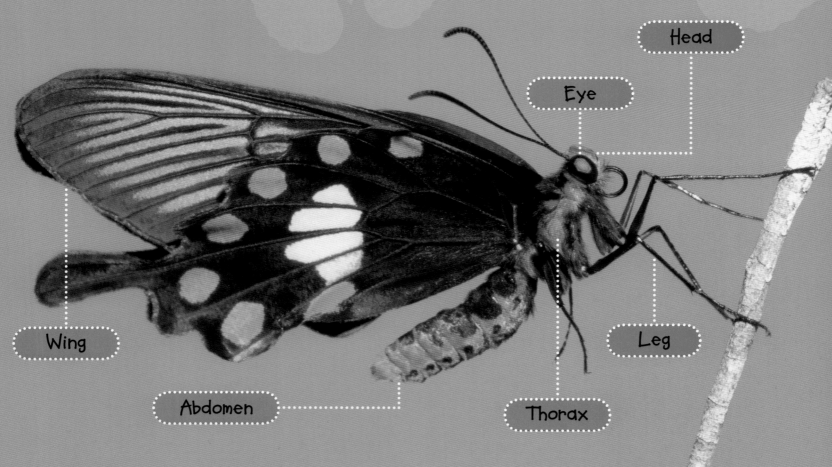

Head

Eye

Wing

Leg

Abdomen

Thorax

The **thorax** is the middle part,
where the legs and wings are attached.
The **abdomen** is the back part, where
the insect **digests** its food.

The story of a butterfly

Butterflies flutter around the plants. Female butterflies look for a place to lay their eggs.

The eggs will hatch into caterpillars. Later, the caterpillars will change into butterflies.

2

Caterpillar

1

Egg

⇧ A butterfly has four stages in its life cycle.

3

The story of how an egg grows into an adult butterfly is called a **life cycle**.

Pupa

4

Adult

A new life begins

In spring, a female butterfly searches for somewhere safe to lay her eggs.

She lays them under the leaves, where they are hidden from view.

Egg

⇨Monarch butterflies lay their eggs on milkweed plants. The eggs stick to the leaves.

8

Different types of butterfly lay their eggs on different plants. Peacock butterflies choose nettles. These plants have stinging hairs. The stings stop animals from eating the nettles and the eggs.

⇨Nettles are a safe place for peacock butterflies to lay their eggs.

The eggs hatch

A few days later, the eggs hatch, and a tiny yellow caterpillar comes out of each one.

Caterpillars spend most of their time eating, so they grow quickly.

⇧Monarch caterpillars become stripy as they grow older.

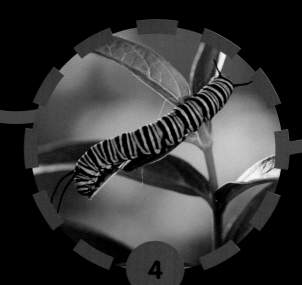

As a caterpillar grows, its skin becomes too tight, and splits. The caterpillar sheds its skin, revealing a new one underneath. This is called **moulting**.

A caterpillar is also known as a **larva**.

⇐ When a caterpillar moults, it wriggles out of its old skin.

1

2

3

5

Staying alive

Caterpillars are soft and juicy – so lots of other animals want to eat them. Many caterpillars have special ways of staying alive.

Monarch caterpillars are bad to eat. Their stripes warn animals that they are **poisonous**.

⇐The monarch caterpillar's poison comes from the milkweed plants it eats.

12

Many caterpillars are green, so they blend in with their surroundings.

This is called **camouflage**.

⇩A green caterpillar on a green leaf can be hard to see.

⇩Some caterpillars have sharp spines on their bodies.

13

Making a pupa

Caterpillars grow fast. After about 14 days, a caterpillar is ready to change into a **pupa**. This is the next stage of its life cycle.

1

✍A caterpillar makes a silk thread, and uses it to hang from a leaf.

2

✍It moults for one last time. The pupa is already formed under the caterpillar's skin.

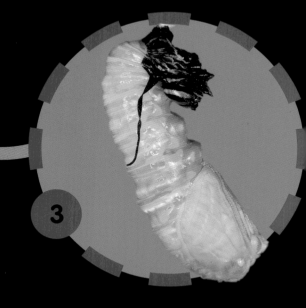

3

✍Once the skin is shed the pupa hardens.

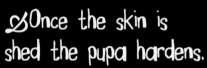

14

A pupa is usually green or grey, so it is difficult to see on a plant. This is another example of camouflage.

5

4

⇦ Inside the pupa, the caterpillar gradually changes.

⇦ The pupa is tough on the outside to protect the insect inside.

15

A butterfly appear

After about two weeks, the pupa of the monarch butterfly becomes darker in colour.

3

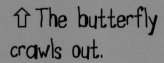
⇧ The butterfly crawls out.

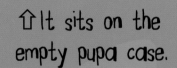
⇧ It sits on the empty pupa case.

2

⇧ The pupa cracks open.

1

⇐ The orange wings of the butterfly can be seen inside.

16

5

6

⇧Then it spreads its wings so they can dry.

Male's dark spot

⇧It has to rest for a few hours before it can fly.

An adult butterfly does not grow any more. Male and female monarchs look similar, but males have small dark spots on their back wings.

17

Butterfly life

Butterflies flutter around, searching for food. They feed on sweet sugary **nectar** inside flowers.

When it is time to mate, the males follow the females. They fly around the females and push them to the ground.

⇨ The female lays her eggs one at a time.

Once the butterflies have mated, the female lays her eggs. A new life cycle then begins.

⇦ Adults usually live for only two to five weeks.

19

A long journey

As the summer comes to an end, monarch butterflies start an amazing journey, called a **migration**.

They fly to warmer places. The journey can cover thousands of kilometres and takes more than two months.

⇧Millions of monarch butterflies spend the winter resting on trees.

In spring, the butterflies set off to their summer homes. On the way, they mate. Their young change into butterflies and continue the journey.

⇧ The monarch butterflies wake up when warm weather arrives.

21

Glossary

Abdomen
The back part of an insect's body.

Camouflage
Patterns and colours that help
an animal to hide.

Digest
When food is digested, it is changed
so the body can use it to get energy.
Animals need energy to live and grow.

Insect
An animal with six legs and a body
divided into three parts.

Larva
Another name for caterpillar.

Life cycle
The story of how a living thing
changes from birth to death and
how it produces young.

Migration
A long journey
made by an animal
or a group of animals.

Moulting
When an insect sheds, or gets rid
of, its old skin.

Nectar
A sweet liquid made by flowers to
attract insects to them.

Poisonous
Harmful to eat. Poison can kill
living things.

Pupa
The life stage when a caterpillar
changes into an adult butterfly.

Thorax
The part of an insect's body between
the head and abdomen.

22

Index

Notes for parents and teachers

- Look through the book and talk about the pictures.

- Safety. Teach children how to keep safe while investigating animals and their life cycles. For example, they can be shown how to recognize plants and animals that sting, or are poisonous.

- Respect for wildlife. Teach children how to observe animals and, if appropriate, handle them with care. They should observe animals in their natural environment, without disturbing them or their habitats.

- Butterfly activities. Drawing, colouring and labelling help children to identify ways that caterpillars and adults are different. Make models together to demonstrate the stages of a butterfly's life cycle.

- Visiting a wildlife garden or butterfly sanctuary helps children to understand the importance of habitats. Explain the way a habitat can provide shelter and food for lots of different animals and plants.

- Be prepared for questions about human life cycles. There are plenty of books for this age group that can help you to give age-appropriate explanations.

- Talking about a child's family helps them to link life processes, such as reproduction, to their own experience. Drawing simple family trees, looking at family photo albums and sharing family stories with grandparents are fun ways to engage young children.